Martin Luther immediately gave his life to Christ becoming a born-again Christian.

Although the exact time of Luther's convers[ion] uncertain, as he searched the Scriptures, h[e] upon a truth that set the tone for the Reform[ation] doctrine of **"Justification."**

Justification is whenever God saves a person from their sin. He justifies them and accepts them as one of his children. He frees them from guilt by making them innocent. God makes us righteous (sinless) when we place our faith in Jesus and His death for us on the cross.

A dad explained Justification to his son like this: "It is when God treats sinners

 as if they have never done anything wrong, providing they have put their faith in Jesus asking Him to forgive their sins."

When a person places their faith in Jesus Christ, they will naturally want to obey God and do good works. However, the good works they do cannot make them right with God; only believing in Jesus Christ, God's Son, can. After we trust in Jesus and turn away from our sin, God forgives us and forgets about those wrong things we have done in the past.

Luther became convinced that the church was corrupt in its ways and had lost sight of several central truths of Christianity such as justification.

Jesus died in our place as our Substitute to pay for our sins so we can be justified by faith.

Luther came to understand justification as entirely the work of God. He wrote that Christians receive righteousness entirely from outside themselves; that righteousness not only comes from Christ but *is* the righteousness of Christ, attributed to Christians through faith.

Faith, for Luther, was a gift from God. The experience of being justified by faith was, in his words, "as though I had been born again." His entry into Heaven no less, was a discovery about "the righteousness of God" – a discovery that "the just person" of whom the Bible speaks, **in Romans 1:17,** lives by faith. Luther believed as the Bible teaches, that Jesus Christ died for our sins and was raised again for our justification **(Romans 3:24–25).** He alone is the Lamb of God who takes away "the sin of the world" **(John 1:29),** and God has laid on Him "the iniquity of us all" **(Isaiah 53:6).** All have sinned and are justified freely, without their works and merits, by His grace, through the redemption that is in Christ Jesus, in His blood **(Romans 3:23–25).** It's necessary to believe this and understand salvation cannot be obtained or grasped by any other work, law or merit. Therefore, it is clear and certain that this faith alone justifies us.

Luther's rediscovery of "Christ and His Salvation" is the foundation for the Reformation. The term Protestant means "to protest," and Luther's writings and his translation of the Bible into the German language started the Protestant faith. His protest at the Sale of Indulgences (pardons) drove him to write his 95 Theses, or arguments, spread across Europe, with people coming to understand "The Just shall live by faith alone." Luther protested against the teaching and practices of the Roman Catholic Church, in particular, the Sale of Indulgences.

Faith, for Luther, was a gift from God.

The Monk Searching For God

The Sale of Indulgences

Martin Luther realised that this practice was being used to take advantage of the poor people who belonged to the church. The Pope needed money to rebuild St Peter's church in Rome, so he sent priests out and about to sell Indulgences. An indulgence, or pardon, was a piece of paper which the priests falsely claimed would ensure that a loved one who had died would go to Heaven or spend less time in Purgatory. Purgatory is believed by Roman Catholics to be a place, or state of suffering, inhabited by the souls of sinners who are making atonement for their sins before going to Heaven.

The priest responsible for selling Indulgences was a man called Johann Tetzel, who would say to the people, "As soon as the coin in the coffer rings the soul from purgatory springs." This was deceiving the people as the Bible does not teach us about a place called purgatory, there is no such place.

These practices went unquestioned during the Middle Ages

One of the most corrupt church practices was the selling of indulgences

Indulges began as a way for people to repent for their sins through good works

But rather than requiring good deeds, church leaders began selling indulgence certificates as a way of raising money

A person can only get to Heaven by being saved through faith in Christ and His finished work on the Cross. They must come to faith during their lifetime. A dead person cannot get saved. It is not an ongoing or uncompleted work; the Bible makes it clear it's a finished work!

Martin Luther started to write down reasons why the Sale of Indulgences was wrong. He listed 95 reasons why he disagreed with this practice; for example, it gave people false assurance that they would not spend eternity in Hell. The Catholic Church was deceitful with the people and stole their money. Luther wanted to expose the Church's corruption.

The 95 Theses

On 31st October 1517, Martin Luther nailed his famous 95 Theses to the door of the Castle Church in Wittenberg.

The Roman Catholic Church taught that faith alone is not sufficient to justify man. They showed that faith must accompany good works, such as donating to the church. Luther's message, however, was the message of the Bible "The Just shall live by faith." **(Romans 1:17).**

By nailing the 95 Theses to the door of Wittenberg Castle Church Luther hoped to encourage discussion and debate among the students at the University of Wittenberg.

He argued that Christ, not the Pope, should be the Head of the Church. Indulgences were meaningless as they gave the people a false hope of Heaven. Salvation is a gift; we cannot earn it or buy it. He wanted to tell people they didn't need a priest to go between them and God, Christ is the only true Mediator. He argued that the Bible and church services should be in the language of the people, not Latin where no one could understand it.

The 95 Theses would later become the foundation of the Protestant Reformation. They were written in a remarkably gracious way, questioning rather than accusing. The first two of the theses contained Luther's central idea, that God intended believers to seek repentance and that faith alone, not works would lead to salvation. The other 93 thesis, directly criticizing the practice of Indulgences, supported the first two.

he 95 Theses were quickly distributed throughout Germany and throughout Europe eventually making their way to Rome. Here are some of them to give you an idea of what Luther was saying:

1. *When Jesus said "repent" he meant that believers should live a whole life repenting.*
2. *Only God can give salvation – not a priest.*
4. *Sin will always remain until we enter Heaven.*
5. *Only God can forgive – not a priest.*
10. *The priest must not threaten those dying with the penalty of purgatory.*
16. *Purgatory = Hell. Heaven = Assurance.*
21. *An Indulgence will not save a man.*
22. *A dead soul can't get saved by an Indulgence.*
24. *Therefore most people are being deceived by Indulgences.*
27. *It is nonsense to teach that money can save a dead soul in Purgatory.*
28. *Money causes greed – only God can save souls.*
33. *Do not believe those who say that a Papal Indulgence is a wonderful gift which allows salvation.*
36. *A man can be free of sin if he sincerely repents – an indulgence is not needed.*
43. *A Christian who gives to the poor or lends to those in need is doing better in God's eyes than one who 'buys forgiveness.'*
45. *A person who passes by a beggar but buys an Indulgence will gain the anger and disappointment of God.*
46. *A Christian should buy what is necessary for life not waste money on an Indulgence.*
47. *Christians do not need an Indulgence.*
48. *The pope should have more desire for faithful prayer than for ready money.*
49. *Christians should be taught not to rely on an Indulgence. They should never lose their fear of God through them.*
50. *If a Pope knew the price people paid for an Indulgence – he would prefer to demolish St. Peter's.*
66. *Indulgences become net income for the wealthy.*
75. *It is wrong to think that papal pardons have the power to absolve all sin.*
77. *Not even St. Peter could remove guilt.*
84. *Evil men must not buy their salvation, when a poor man who is a friend of God, cannot.*
89. *Why are Indulgences only issued when the Pope sees fit to release them?*
94. *Christians must follow Christ at all cost.*

Recant

THE POPE WARNED LUTHER IN A LETTER THAT HE RISKED EXCOMMUNICATION from the Catholic Church if he did not recant (withdraw and apologise for) his writings, including the 95 Theses. Expulsion followed by the Pope after Luther burned the letter.

The assembly of the Holy Roman Empire brought Luther before them in a town called Worms. Known as "The Diet of Worms" Luther was presented with copies of his writings and books and asked if they were his and if he stood by what he had written. He prayed, consulted friends, and gave his response the next day.

"Unless I am convinced by the testimony of the Scriptures or by clear reason (for I do not trust either in the Pope or councils alone since they have often erred and contradicted themselves), I am held captive by the Scriptures I have quoted, and my conscience is captive to the Word of God. I cannot and will not recant anything since it is neither safe nor right to go against conscience. Here I stand, I can do no other. May God help me, Amen!"

Over the next five days, private conferences were held to determine Luther's fate. The Emperor presented the final draft of the Edict of Worms on 25th May 1521, declaring Luther an outlaw, banning his literature, and ordering his arrest: "We want him to be apprehended and punished as a notorious heretic." It also made it a crime for anyone in Germany to give Luther food or shelter.

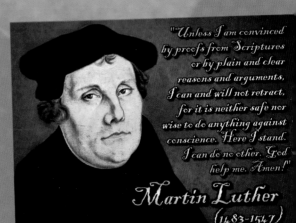

"Unless I am convinced by proofs from Scriptures or by plain and clear reasons and arguments, I can and will not retract, for it is neither safe nor wise to do anything against conscience. Here I stand. I can do no other. God help me. Amen!"

Martin Luther
(1483-1547)

At Wartburg Castle

I love this part of Luther's story. Luther's life was in danger now, great danger! On his way back to Wittenberg he was kidnapped by masked horsemen as he journeyed through the forest. However, this was a clever ploy arranged by Frederick III and Luther's friends. It was made to look like a robbery, but it was actually to save his life.

Translation of the Bible

Luther found a safe place in Wartburg Castle. During his year there, he translated the New Testament into German, the local language. Up until then, most people had never read the Bible. Church services were in Latin, and people knew so little about God, or the truth of the gospel, that Luther knew he wanted Germans to be able to read about God for themselves.

The Printing Press

The relatively new invention of the printing press provided the means to spread copies of the Bible and Christian literature throughout Germany and the rest of Europe. Luther initially wrote many books and sermons using a quill and inkwell. The printing press meant that the time required to reproduce copies of these became dramatically reduced. Millions of copies swept across Europe at that point. In fact, much of his writing is still available online today!

Worship and singing

Martin Luther is famous for being the author of many hymns such as "A mighty fortress is our God." He re-introduced singing in church and encouraged it in schools, emphasising that it was an important part of worshipping God and often accompanied hymn singing with the flute.

The Runaway Nun

Martin Luther married Katharina von Bora, one of 12 nuns he had helped escape from a convent smuggled out in herring barrels. Several of the other nuns married priests.

Luther said "Suddenly, and while occupied with far different thoughts, the Lord has plunged me into marriage." From reading the Bible, he realised that anyone had the right to marry and it was God's way of bringing children into the world.

At the time of their marriage, Katharina was 26 years old, and Luther was 41 years old. The couple had six children of their own and also adopted more children. They used their home as bed and breakfast and farmed a little to help make ends meet.

The Runaway Nun!

The Five Solas

THE FIVE SOLAS ARE FIVE LATIN SAYINGS THAT EMERGED FROM THE PROTESTANT REFORMATION that contrast the Reformers' theological principles with the teachings of the Roman Catholic Church. The word "Sola" means "alone" or "only" as seen in the following phrases:

Sola Fide, by faith alone.
Sola Scriptura, by Scripture alone.
Solus Christus, through Christ alone.
- *Sola Gratia,* by grace alone.
- *Soli Deo Gloria,* glory to God alone.

HE 5 SOLAS
HE REFORMATION

SOLA GRATIA
Grace Alone

SOLA FIDE
Faith Alone

OLUS CHRISTUS
Christ Alone

OLI DEO GLORIA
Glory of God Alone

OLA SCRIPTURA
Scripture Alone

NABLETHEOLOGY.ORG/FIVE-SOLAS

These phrases may be found individually expressed in the various writings of the 16th-century Reformers. These are <u>Christian</u> theological rules that distinguish most <u>Protestant</u> churches from the Roman <u>Catholic</u> <u>Church</u>.

FAITH ALONE (Sola Fide) also known as **justification by faith alone**.

When we think of the word faith, we think of confidence, belief, conviction, assurance and trust. Faith is completely trusting and relying on Jesus Christ's finished work on the cross, believing that it alone is enough to redeem us from our sins. There is nothing we can do to make ourselves better or more acceptable.

SCRIPTURE ALONE (Sola Scriptura)

Scripture is the written word of God, which teaches us all we need to know about Him. The Scripture contains all instructions necessary for our salvation and is the standard by which all Christian behaviour gets measured. The Bible alone enables us to know God personally and teaches us how to live to please Him.

CHRIST ALONE (Solus Christus)

Our salvation is made possible by what Jesus Christ accomplished on the cross. His perfect, sinless life, death, and resurrection, is sufficient alone for our salvation. Through Christ, we are accepted (justified) and reconciled (reunited) to God the Father.

GRACE ALONE (Sola Gratia)

In salvation, we receive God's grace alone. GRACE (God's riches at Christ's expense.) is the supernatural work of the Holy Spirit which brings us to Christ, releasing us from our burden of sin and raising us from spiritual death to spiritual life.

GLORY TO GOD ALONE (Soli Deo Gloria)

God's glory is his Magnificence, Splendour, Beauty, Wonder, Brilliance and Grandeur. Salvation is a gift from God alone. Our primary aim in life should be to glorify God and enjoy Him every day. We are to be motivated and inspired by the glory of God and not seek our glory.

THE EARLY REFORMERS

Key differences between Catholic and Protestant beliefs

CATHOLIC PRACTICE AND BELIEF	PROTESTANT PRACTICE AND BELIEF
Pray to Mary	Pray to God
Pray to Saints	Pray to God
Go to the priest for forgiveness	Ask God to forgive
Believe in Purgatory	Only Heaven & Hell
Don't have assurance of eternal life	Christians have assurance of eternal life
Words of Pope equally important to the Bible	Bible is the only authority
Pray for the dead	Don't pray for the dead
Salvation is faith plus works	Salvation is faith alone

The Story of Martin Luther

O	R	E	D	L	N	F	D	N	H	I	M	R	R
P	E	R	S	O	E	O	A	H	S	P	B	N	S
R	B	T	C	E	O	C	N	I	E	B	R	N	E
O	O	I	H	C	I	R	O	G	S	N	T	N	C
T	T	C	I	S	U	M	R	I	E	U	C	S	N
E	C	C	H	R	I	S	T	G	H	A	H	A	E
S	O	T	L	I	B	H	O	E	T	S	S	L	G
T	L	D	T	C	I	L	O	H	T	A	C	V	L
A	N	M	T	S	R	M	A	R	T	I	N	A	U
N	E	D	U	C	A	T	I	O	N	E	O	T	D
T	S	C	O	E	P	O	B	S	N	L	B	I	N
H	T	I	A	F	E	E	I	A	A	B	E	O	I
Y	N	A	M	R	E	G	T	C	A	I	O	N	I
R	A	L	U	T	H	E	R	U	T	B	O	O	A

BIBLE
LUTHER
SALVATION
INDULGENCES
MARTIN
THESES
EDUCATION
GERMANY
MUSIC
DOOR
CHRIST
CATHOLIC
PROTESTANT
OCTOBER
FAITH

Martin Luther Word Search

```
X H E H C A S T L E P B J D F G
X F O S U R Z P L O P T B P D C
Q R H C T K C C Y L S L G K L P
X G Q J D O O N X R N Z Y L O N
Z B E A F R R E Q O U Q U P B T
O Q T E M M E M S Z N Q K R I H
J U S T I F I C A T I O N I B E
R E F O R M A T I O N J R N L S
J C U D F I W I W L L D F T E I
U J E Y I V E X R I P M N I I S
B B J N W R T C Q L V Y N N B Q
R O M A N S U H G U I Y I G M R
N Z E M C H R I S T V K T M O G
B H E R E C A N T H K J R V N Q
R O K E X V O W B E M S A K K P
C W Z G F O K W R R F W M M K S
```

Martin	Luther	Reformation	Nun	Justification
Storm	Printing	Bible	Germany	Monk
Thesis	Recant	Castle	Christ	Romans

13

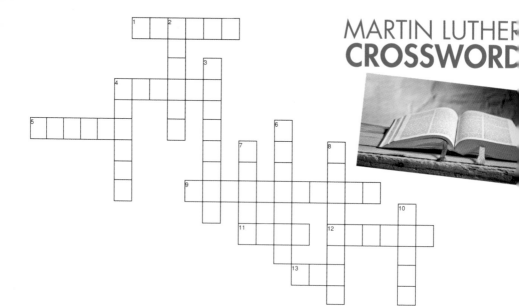

MARTIN LUTHER CROSSWORD

Across

1. Book in the New Testament
4. Luther hid here
5. Martin's surname
9. To reform
11. A friar
12. There were 95 of these
13. Luther married one of these

Down

2. Luther's first name
3. A person who reforms
4. Died for our sins
6. A country in Europe
7. When the weather gets bad
8. Reproduction of a book
10. God's word

HERE I STAND

MARTIN LUTHER

The Reformation

LUTHER 500 YEARS OF THE REFORMATION

74